Contents

1.1 What's the book about?

What do you know about earthquakes? Talk to other students and make notes here.

Notes

The ground moves.

1.2 What happens first?

1 **Look at the picture on page 1. What do you think?**

a What is the young man thinking?

....

b What is the young woman thinking?

....

2 **Look at the picture on page 2.**

a What is the younger man thinking?

....

b What is the older man thinking?

....

c Which man do you like more? Why?

....

The Earthquake

Elizabeth Laird

Level 2

Series Editors: Andy Hopkins and Jocelyn Potter

Pearson Education Limited
Edinburgh Gate, Harlow,
Essex CM20 2JE, England
and Associated Companies throughout the world.

ISBN: 978-1-4082-0951-6

First edition published 2000
This edition published 2009

1 3 5 7 9 10 8 6 4 2

Text copyright © Penguin Books Ltd 2000
This edition copyright © Pearson Education Ltd 2009
Illustrations by Rafa Fonteriz

The moral rights of the authors have been asserted in accordance with
the Copyright Designs and Patents Act 1988

Set in 12/15.5pt A. Garamond
Printed in China
SWTC/01
Produced for the Publishers by AC Estudio Editorial S.L.

Published by Pearson Education Ltd in association with Penguin Books Ltd,
both companies being subsidiaries of Pearson Plc

For a complete list of the titles available in the Penguin Active Reading series please write to your local
Pearson Longman office or to: Penguin Readers Marketing Department, Pearson Education,
Edinburgh Gate, Harlow, Essex CM20 2JE, England.

CHAPTER 1

Two Tickets

'I want to tell you something about Marco. He's rich, but he's a bad man. You're being stupid, Silvia.'

G abriel had a kind face and intelligent brown eyes. He usually had a friendly smile. But there was no smile on his face today. He wasn't happy.

'I'd like to be as rich as Marco,' he thought. 'But I'm only good old Gabriel. Silvia likes me. I know she does. She thinks I'm kind and nice. But she thinks I'm boring too. Boring old Gabriel, that's me.'

Gabriel had two tickets for a film. There was a red **rose** on the table in his sitting-room. He took the rose and the tickets and went out.

◆

An hour later, Gabriel arrived at the door of Silvia's flat. When she opened the door, she didn't smile at him.

'Oh, hello,' she said. 'What ... er ... ?'

rose /rəʊz/ (n) A *rose* is a beautiful garden flower. There are red roses, white roses, and roses in other colours too.

'Don't you remember, Silvia?' said Gabriel. 'It's Sunday evening. We're going to the cinema. I've got the tickets. It's that great new film. You said ...'

'What do you mean?' said Silvia. 'I can't go out with you this evening. I'm busy. I don't remember ...'

'But I called you on Thursday!' Gabriel said. 'You wanted to come!'

Silvia pushed her beautiful dark hair out of her eyes. She didn't look at Gabriel.

'Oh dear,' she said. 'That was stupid of me. I'm really sorry. Please don't be angry, Gabriel. Come back tomorrow. We'll go to the film tomorrow.'

She began to shut the door.

'Silvia,' Gabriel said angrily, 'you're going out with Marco! I know you are! I want to tell you something about Marco. He's rich, but he's a bad man. You're being stupid, Silvia.'

He stopped. Silvia wasn't there. 'I'm talking to the door,' he thought

angrily. He looked at the rose in his hand. Then he threw it onto the ground.

Behind him, he heard a quiet laugh. He turned. There was a man on the stairs. His clothes were expensive, and there were twenty red roses in his hand. It was Marco.

'Oh dear, Gabriel,' Marco laughed. 'Is she busy tonight? Doesn't she want to go out with you? *I'll* try now. Perhaps she'll go out with *me*.'

Gabriel didn't answer. He walked quickly away and went down to the street.

It was a hot Sunday evening. There was no wind. A lot of people were in the street. They sat in the parks and drank in the cafés. Young men and women talked and laughed. Gabriel didn't want to look at them. He felt too unhappy.

He took out the two tickets.

'I paid for them,' he thought, 'and it's a wonderful film. I'll go without her! I'm not going to think about Silvia Delgado. I'll go and see the film, and I'll enjoy it.'

The Plaza cinema was a big, old building in the centre of town. The doors weren't open, so there were a lot of people outside. Gabriel waited with them.

When the doors opened, people went quickly inside to the ticket office. But Gabriel had his ticket, so he waited outside.

It was 8.27 p.m. And at that minute, the **earthquake** happened.

---

earthquake /ˈɜːθkweɪk/ (n) When there is an *earthquake*, the ground moves. Buildings often move too.

CHAPTER 2

A Table for Two

Marco didn't know about the Delgados' money. He saw their pictures,
their jewellery and other expensive things, and he liked them all.

Marco stood at the door of Silvia's flat and watched Gabriel leaving. He looked carefully at his clothes and his shoes. Why didn't Silvia open the door? She was in there. Then, suddenly, it opened.

'Silvia, dear,' Marco said, 'you look wonderful ...'

He stopped. Silvia didn't look wonderful. Her face was red, and she looked unhappy.

'Gabriel said something to her,' Marco thought. 'What was it? That young man doesn't like me, and *I* don't like *him.*'

He followed Silvia into the sitting-room.

'I'm nearly ready,' she said. 'Have a drink. I'll come in a minute.'

Marco knew the Delgados' sitting-room well. He went to the table and got a drink. Then he sat down in an expensive armchair. He liked the flat. There were beautiful pictures on the walls, and everything in the room looked very expensive.

Silvia lived with her mother. Her father was dead. Before he died, Mr Delgado had a good job. He had cars and friends and a lot of money. But the Delgados weren't a rich family now, and Silvia's mother was ill. The doctor often came and visited her. Sometimes, Mrs Delgado had to go to hospital. She had to have good food and expensive **medicine**s. The Delgados didn't have much money now.

---

medicine /ˈmedsən/ (n) You take *medicine* when you feel ill.

Marco didn't know about the Delgados' money. He saw their pictures, their **jewellery** and other expensive things, and he liked them all.

'Silvia!' Mrs Delgado called weakly from her bedroom. 'Are you there, dear? What are you doing? Is somebody with you? Who is it?'

Marco heard Silvia's answer. 'It's all right, Mother,' she said. 'It's only Gabriel. We're going to see a film.'

'Ah!' thought Marco. 'So Mrs Delgado doesn't like me! Mrs Delgado likes dear Gabriel!'

He went back to the table and had another drink.

'Perhaps you don't like me, Mrs Delgado,' Marco thought. 'But your daughter does. Oh, yes. She likes me very much.' He smiled.

Ten minutes later, Silvia came into the room again. Her dark hair was beautiful. Her big, brown eyes were excited. Her dress was very pretty. She smiled happily.

'Hello, Marco,' she said. 'I'm ready now.'

He put down his glass and stood up.

'We're going to have a wonderful, wonderful evening,' he said.

◆

Outside, it was very hot. Marco drove his car fast. Silvia felt the wind in her hair. It was good.

jewellery /ˈdʒuːəlri/ (n) You wear *jewellery* – on your clothes or fingers, perhaps – because you want to look nice.

'Gabriel hasn't got a car,' thought Silvia. She turned and looked at Marco. 'Where are we going?' she asked.

'I'm taking you to the Oasis Restaurant,' Marco said. 'It's the best restaurant in town. It's very expensive, of course, but nothing is too good for you, Silvia. I know a lot of girls, but you're the most beautiful.'

The Oasis Restaurant was two kilometres outside the town. There were a lot of big cars outside it. Marco pushed open the doors. Inside, it was nearly dark. There were pretty little lights on the tables, and a man played quiet music. Some people danced.

'Good evening, sir,' the **manager** said to Marco.

'I called this afternoon,' said Marco. 'I want a table for two.'

'Of course. Please follow me,' the manager said.

Marco and Silvia followed him to the back of the restaurant. Their table was near the door to the kitchen. Waiters went in and out with food and drink.

manager /ˈmænɪdʒə/ (n) The *manager* is the boss in an office or in another workplace.

Marco looked at the manager angrily. 'I don't want this table,' he said. 'We're going to dance later. We want to be near the dancing. I have to have a better table.'

'I'm sorry, sir,' said the manager. 'I can't do that. We're busy this evening. Come early next time. Then I can put you near the dancing.' He began to walk away.

'Wait a minute,' said Marco. 'I'm not happy with this. You've got to ...'

'I'm very sorry,' said the manager again. 'I can't give you a better table now. Later, perhaps ...'

'But ...' said Marco.

People began to turn round and look at Marco. Silvia looked at the floor. Marco always did this. He always wanted the best place in the restaurant, in the theatre or at the football game. Silvia put her hand on Marco's arm.

'This table's OK,' she said. 'I don't want to change. Why ... ?'

'Be quiet, my dear,' said Marco. 'Leave this to me.' He turned back to the manager. 'Now,' he said, 'you listen to me.'

'Everybody's watching us now,' thought Silvia. She caught his arm again. 'I'll see you in a minute,' she said. 'I'm going to the washroom.'

She walked between the tables to a door at the other end of the restaurant. She saw young men and women dancing. Older people laughed and talked. They all looked happy.

The washroom was outside the restaurant, in a small garden. Silvia opened the door and walked into the garden.

It was 8.27 p.m. And at that minute, the earthquake happened.

2.1 Were you right?

Look back at your answers to Activity 1.2 on page iv. Then finish these sentences.

> Gabriel likes Silvia, but she doesn't really want to go to the
> 1....................... with him. She wants to go out with 2........................ .
> He is a 3....................... man with 4....................... clothes. Gabriel
> thinks that he is a 5....................... man. He thinks that Silvia is
> being 6....................... . Marco knows that she likes him
> 7....................... than Gabriel. He 8....................... at Gabriel.

2.2 What more did you learn?

1 What happens first? Write the numbers, 1–6.

○   **a**   Marco drives Silvia to the Oasis Restaurant.

○   **b**   Silvia goes to the washroom outside the restaurant.

○   **c**   Marco looks at the Delgados' expensive pictures.

○   **d**   Marco speaks angrily to the restaurant manager.

○   **e**   Silvia tells her mother that she is going out with Gabriel.

○   **f**   There is an earthquake.

2 When the earthquake starts, where is:

a   Gabriel?   ....

b   Silvia?   ....

c   Marco?   ....

d   Mrs Delgado?   ....

.3 Language in use

Look at the sentences in the box. Then make the sentences below into one sentence. Put *when* at the beginning of each sentence or in the middle.

> **When** she opened the door, she didn't smile at him.
>
> **When** the doors opened, people went quickly inside.

1 Gabriel left his flat. Gabriel took a rose and two tickets.

   When Gabriel left his flat, he took a rose and two tickets.

2 He arrived at Silvia's flat. Silvia wasn't very friendly.

   ....

3 Marco laughed at Gabriel. He saw Gabriel outside Silvia's door.

   ....

4 Gabriel went to the cinema. Gabriel left Silvia's flat.

   ....

5 Marco saw their table. He was angry with the manager.

   ....

6 Everybody in the restaurant looked happy. Silvia went outside.

   ....

2.4 What happens next?

Look at the words at the bottom of pages 10 and 11. What is Silvia going to see and hear? Write four of the words under these pictures.

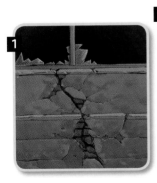

CHAPTER 3

Silvia's Story

Suddenly, the lights went out, and it was nearly dark. Then people started to scream. Silvia didn't move. She couldn't move.

The ground moved under Silvia's feet.

'Help! What is it? What's happening?' she thought.

There was a **terrible** noise, and she looked up into the sky. Perhaps the noise and the **shaking** came from a plane.

Suddenly, the lights went out, and it was nearly dark. Then people started to **scream**. Silvia didn't move. She couldn't move.

'It's an earthquake,' she thought. 'Oh, no, please, no!'

The ground moved again. A long **crack** started to run up from the bottom of the wall in front of her to the top. Then the wall opened, and Silvia could see the people inside the restaurant. They tried to run. Their screams were terrible. She could see hands pushing and pulling. She could see their faces and their eyes. They were terribly afraid.

Then the wall fell, and the **roof** came down. Silvia couldn't see the faces and hands now. The Oasis Restaurant wasn't there. It was only **rubble**.

Silvia couldn't move. She couldn't scream.

'Marco's in there!' she thought. 'Marco, and the manager, and ... and those people. They ... Oh, I can't ... I don't ...'

terrible /ˈterəbəl/ (adj) A *terrible* thing is a very bad thing. When you are *terribly* happy, you are very happy.
shake /ʃeɪk/ (v) When something *shakes*, it moves a little, but quickly and many times.
scream /skriːm/ (v/n) You *scream* when you are afraid. A scream is a very loud, high noise.
crack /kræk/ (n) When there is a *crack* across something, it is breaking.
roof /ruːf/ (n) The *roof* is the top of a house. It sits on the walls.
rubble /ˈrʌbəl/ (n) After a heavy building falls to the ground, there is only *rubble* there.

There was another loud noise behind her. Silvia turned. Another building fell. And another. And another.

Suddenly, she remembered her mother.

◆

Silvia tried to get out of the garden into the street, but it wasn't easy. She had to climb over a **broken** wall. She couldn't climb in her evening shoes. She took them off and carried them in her hand. She got up to the top of the wall and fell down into the street. Her pretty dress was dirty now, and she had cuts on her feet.

There were people everywhere. They ran up and down the street and screamed. Some people tried to pull the rubble away from a building.

'Come and help!' one of them said to Silvia. 'My little boy's under there. Help me, please!'

'I'm sorry,' said Silvia. 'I have to find my mother.'

There were cars everywhere too. Everybody wanted to get away from the buildings and out into the country.

'Stop! Take me with you! Take me home!' she screamed at them. But they didn't hear her. They didn't stop.

broken /ˈbrəʊkən/ (adj) When something is *broken*, you can't use it.

'I'll have to walk,' she thought. 'It's a long way, but I can do it. I have to go home and help my mother. I have to!'

Silvia began to run. It wasn't easy. There was rubble across the road. A roof fell to the ground behind her. A wall suddenly fell in front of her. She climbed over it and started to run again.

It wasn't dark now. The sky was red and black with fires and thick, black smoke.

Silvia had only one idea in her head. There was nobody with her mother. She was ill in her bed. She couldn't move easily. Perhaps she was hurt. Perhaps she was ...

'No!' thought Silvia. 'She's not dead! Oh, please, no, please! She's all right. I know she is! Mother! Mother!'

She was in the centre of town now. She looked round the square. There were some houses, and the big church clock showed the right time. But the hotel next to it was only a **ruin**.

The Plaza was in the same square. For the first time, Silvia stopped and watched. Firemen and policemen carried people out of the cinema.

'What happened?' she asked a girl.

'The roof fell,' the girl said. 'Hundreds of people are dead.'

'Perhaps Gabriel didn't go,' thought Silvia. 'Or perhaps he came too late, or ...' She didn't want to think about Gabriel now. The idea was too terrible.

---

ruin /ˈruːɪn/ (n) A *ruin* is a building after the top or one or two walls fall down.

The Delgados' building was near the town centre, at the end of a street. Silvia began to run again. She could see a big fire. She could hear people screaming.

The building next to the Delgados' home was a ruin. Men and women pulled at the rubble. Silvia knew them. They were her **neighbour**s. They wanted to find their families and friends. But the Delgados' building was there. There was a big crack in the front wall, and some windows were broken. But the building looked **safe**.

'Hey, don't go in there!' a man called to Silvia. 'It's too dangerous!'

But Silvia didn't stop. She pushed open the door and went in.

Inside, it was dark. She tried the lights, but they didn't work. Quickly, she ran up the stairs to the flat.

The front door was open.

'Mother!' she called. 'Are you all right? It's me! Mother, where are you?'

She went to her mother's bedroom. The door was open, but there was nobody in the bed. Mrs Delgado wasn't there.

neighbour /ˈneɪbə/ (n) Your *neighbours* are the people in the houses next to yours.
safe /seɪf/ (adj) When you are *safe*, nothing dangerous is going to happen to you.

13

3.1 Were you right?

Look back at Activity 2.4 Then finish the sentences. Write the letters, a–g.

1 People started to scream, ...

2 A long crack started to run up the wall ...

3 The roof came down ...

4 Silvia wanted to find her mother, ...

5 Silvia screamed at the drivers, ...

6 A wall fell in front of her, ...

7 The big church clock showed the right time, ...

---

a so she had to climb over it.	d but Silvia couldn't move.
b and the restaurant was rubble.	e and then the wall opened.
c but the hotel next to it was a ruin.	f so she couldn't look for the little boy.
	g but they didn't hear her.

3.2 What more did you learn?

Why does Silvia worry about her mother ...

1 before she arrives home?

     Nobody is with her.
     ....
     ....

2 after she arrives home?

     ....
     ....
     ....

3.3 Language in use

**Read the sentences in the box.
Then write** *could, couldn't* **or**
had to **in the sentences below.**

> Silvia **could** see the people inside
> the restaurant.
>
> She **had to** climb over a broken wall.

1 She .... take off her shoes.

2 She .... walk because nobody stopped for her.

3 She .... see a big fire.

4 She .... hear people screaming.

5 She .... put on the lights because they didn't work.

6 She .... find her mother in the flat.

3.4 What happens next?

1 What will Silvia do now? What do you think? Circle Yes or No.

    a She will find her mother in the kitchen.   Yes   No

    b She will help her neighbours.   Yes   No

    c She will put on different shoes.   Yes   No

    d She will look for Marco.   Yes   No

2 Look at this picture. What do you think?

    a Who is the old man?

    ....

    ....

    ....

    b How does he feel? Why?

    ....

    ....

    c What will Silvia say to him?

    ....

    ....

CHAPTER 4

Neighbours

'Where's my mother? She's not in our flat. You know she can't walk.
Did somebody take her? Who? Where did they go?'

S ilvia sat down on her mother's bed and cried.
'Where is she?' she thought. 'Who's with her? What can I do?'

She stood up. Her feet hurt, so she went to her bedroom for some better shoes. She started to take off her dress, but then she heard another loud noise. Another building fell.

'I can't stay here inside the building,' she thought. 'It's too dangerous.'

She went quickly out of the flat and down into the street. Then she stopped. 'Where can I go? What can I do?' she thought. First, she had to find her mother. After that – but no, she didn't want to think about Marco. He was in the ruins of the Oasis Restaurant. And she couldn't think about Gabriel. Perhaps he was in the ruins of the Plaza cinema.

Suddenly, she saw a neighbour. The old man lived in the next building. She went to him and put her hand on his arm.

'Oh, Mr Enriques,' she said. 'You're safe.'

The old man didn't move. He didn't see or hear her. His face was white and his hands shook. He started to cry quietly.

Silvia shook his arm.

'Mr Enriques!' she said. 'It's me, Silvia Delgado. Where's my mother? She's not in our flat. You know she can't walk. Did somebody take her? Who? Where did they go?'

The old man turned and looked at her.

'Silvia – Mrs Delgado – I don't know,' he said. 'I can't remember. There was something – yes, I think ... perhaps it was Mr Garcia. Yes, Mr Garcia, the man from the second floor in your building. He carried her down and put her in his car. Yes, that's it. It was Mr Garcia.'

'But where are they?' said Silvia. 'Where did they go?'

'He said something,' said the old man. 'I don't remember. He said, 'Tell Silvia ...'

'Tell me what? Please remember, Mr Enriques. Please!'

'He said ... er ... something about a park,' said Mr Enriques. 'Yes, that was it. "It's safe in the park," he said. He wanted to go away from the buildings. Past the river. To Liberty Park.'

Silvia looked at Mr. Enriques' sad, old face and put her arm round him.

'Thank you, oh, thank you,' she said. 'I'll come back later. I'll help you then.'

'Help me? You can't help me,' said Mr Enriques. 'I haven't got anything now. My wife, my home ...'

◆

Liberty Park was outside the town, past the football ground. Silvia started to walk. Then she stopped. Her mother was old and ill. She had to take her medicines. And they were on the table next to her mother's bed.

It was dangerous, but Silvia didn't think about it. She ran back into the flat. She found a big bag and put into it some warm clothes and her mother's medicine bottles. Then she ran outside again and shut the door behind her.

It was a long way to Liberty Park. Silvia started walking.

Gabriel's Story

Slowly, he started to walk. He felt terribly weak. His right arm hurt very badly, and his head too. Sometimes he nearly fell.

At the time of the earthquake, Gabriel was outside the Plaza. A lot of people wanted to buy their tickets, and they went inside. But he had his ticket. He was safe because he waited outside.

Gabriel heard the first sounds of the earthquake. But he didn't see the buildings when they fell. He didn't hear the screams. Some rubble hit him on the head and he fell to the ground. After a long time, he heard somebody. It was a woman.

'Look at this young man,' the woman said. 'Is he dead?'

'No,' said another woman, 'but he's hurt.'

'I'm – I'm all right,' said Gabriel. He tried to sit up. The women moved away.

Gabriel's arm hurt terribly. He couldn't move it. It was broken. He sat in the street. Then he stood up slowly and looked round. It was nearly dark. Only the cars gave some light.

'My family!' he thought. 'Mum! Dad!'

But they were a long way away in another town. He couldn't do anything for them. Then he thought of Silvia. She was with Marco. He couldn't help her. But there was nobody with Mrs Delgado. And she was ill.

'I'll go back to the Delgados' flat,' thought Gabriel. 'I can help Mrs Delgado, and perhaps I'll hear **news** of Silvia.'

Slowly, he started to walk. He felt terribly weak. His right arm hurt very badly, and his head too. Sometimes he nearly fell.

Hundreds of people were in the street. A woman ran into Gabriel. By accident, she hit his arm. It hurt terribly. He sat down in the road. Everything went black.

When Gabriel opened his eyes again, he felt very ill. He tried to sit up and look round. He wasn't in the street now. He was on the ground with a lot of other people. Doctors and **nurse**s moved quietly round them.

news /njuːz/ (n) After something happens, you want to learn more about it. Then you listen to the *news* on television, or you ask people for news.
nurse /nɛːs/ (n) *Nurses* work with doctors in hospitals.

He tried to feel his head with his hand. Then he remembered his arm. A nurse came to him.

'Where am I? What happened?' he said.

'You're in the garden of the hospital,' she said. 'Your arm's broken, I'm afraid. And you've got a bad cut on your head too. We can't do more for you now. Thousands of people are waiting for help, and we haven't got medicines for all of them. It's not safe inside the hospital, but don't **worry**. You'll be all right here. Stay here quietly and sleep.'

She went away. Gabriel watched her. Then he remembered Silvia. He had to go and find her. He had to help Mrs Delgado. Slowly, he stood up. He was weak, but he could walk. The doctors and nurses didn't see him. They were too busy.

Gabriel left the hospital and started to walk back into town.

worry /ˈwʌri/ (v) You *worry* because you are afraid of something in the future. When you are *worried*, you often don't sleep well.

4.1 Were you right?

Look back at your answers to Activity 3.4. What do you know about Silvia, her mother and Mr Garcia now? Talk to other students and write notes about these people.

Notes

4.2 What more did you learn?

Read these sentences about Gabriel. Are they right (✓) or wrong (✗)?

1 He is safe because he is outside the cinema.

2 Somebody hits Gabriel on the head.

3 He has a broken arm.

4 He wants to find Mrs Delgado and hear about Silvia.

5 When he opens his eyes, he is inside the hospital.

6 The nurse gives him some medicine.

7 Gabriel leaves the hospital.

4.3 Language in use

Look at the sentence in the box. Which words on the right follow the words on the left?

> Her feet hurt, **so** she went to her bedroom for some better shoes.

1 Silvia couldn't stay in the building, so

2 Silvia had to find her mother, so

3 It was safe in the park, so

4 Mrs Delgado had to take her medicines, so

5 Gabriel's arm was broken, so

6 Gabriel's family were in another town, so

a she couldn't think about Marco.

b it hurt terribly.

c Mr Garcia took Mrs Delgado there.

d she went into the street.

e he couldn't help them.

f Silvia took them with her.

4.4 What happens next?

Discuss the pictures in Chapter 6. What is happening? Write one or two sentences about each picture.

1 page 24 ....

....

....

2 page 25 ....

....

....

3 page 26 ....

....

....

4 page 27 ....

....

....

Liberty Park

'We pulled him from the rubble, but did he say, "Thank you"?
No, he didn't! He was only worried about his car.'

S ilvia didn't like walking. She usually caught a bus or took a taxi. She was tired, and her back hurt.

But she didn't think about her back, or about the cuts on her feet. She was with a lot of other people. They all had the same idea. They wanted to leave the town and go into the country, away from the dangerous high buildings.

A friendly woman talked to Silvia.

'Isn't anybody with you, dear?' she said. 'Where's your family?'

'There's only my mother,' said Silvia. 'I think she's at Liberty Park. I'm going to look for her.'

'Don't worry, you'll find her,' the woman said kindly. Silvia felt better.

'Did you see the Grand Hotel?' said a man. 'It's a ruin. Hundreds of people were inside it.'

'It's terrible, terrible,' his wife said. 'I saw a baby ...' She stopped.

'And the shopping centre,' another woman said. 'The shoe shop is all right, but the supermarket is a ruin.'

'The centre's bad,' said a man, 'but it's worse east of here. I was out there when the earthquake happened.'

'Near the station?' the kind woman asked.

'No, near the Oasis Restaurant,' the man said.

Silvia started to listen more carefully.

'The Oasis is a lovely place,' somebody said. 'Is it all right?'

'No,' the man said. 'It's a ruin. A lot of people are dead. But the manager was all right. He was at the back of the restaurant. It was better there. He'll be all right. I wanted to help the other people, but I was worried about my family. So I came back into town. We're all safe. But our home ...' He stopped talking.

Silvia turned to him.

'Excuse me,' she said. 'There was a man in the restaurant – the manager was with him when – when ... the earthquake ... Do you know – is he all right?'

'Yes,' said the man. 'He's all right. I pulled him out. A tall, dark man. Is that him?'

'Yes,' said Silvia.

The man laughed.

'Don't worry about him,' he said. 'He's fine. My friend and I worked hard. We pulled him from the rubble, but did he say, "Thank you"? No,

he didn't! He was only worried about his car. He didn't help the other people under the rubble. He only had small cuts on his face and hands, but he wanted to see a doctor. Other people were dead or nearly dead, but he wasn't interested in them. I'm sorry ... Is he your friend? But, really ...'

Silvia didn't answer him. She wanted to think.

Marco wasn't dead! She was very happy about that, of course. But she understood now. She was stupid. A stupid, stupid girl. She didn't love Marco. She didn't *like* him. She loved Gabriel. And now, perhaps, it was too late.

At midnight, there was another small earthquake. The people in the road screamed. They wanted to run – but where could they go? Behind them, in the town, more buildings fell.

'Oh, no,' thought Silvia. 'When will this end?'

◆

At 12.30 a.m. Silvia arrived at Liberty Park. She looked round. There were thousands of people on the ground. Other people stood and talked. She couldn't see very well in the thick smoke.

'I'll never find Mother here,' thought Silvia. She began to walk up and down the park.

'Mother!' she called. 'Mother, it's me, Silvia! Where are you?'

After an hour, she was very tired. 'I have to sit down,' she thought. 'I'll start again in the morning. But now I'm going to sleep somewhere.'

Then suddenly, she heard her name. She turned round.

'Mr Garcia!' she said. 'Where's Mother?'

'She's here,' said Mr Garcia, 'and she's all right. But she's very worried about you. My wife's with her now. How did you find us?'

'It's a long story,' said Silvia. 'I'll tell you later. But now ...'

'I know,' said Mr Garcia. 'You want your mother. Come with me.'

Mrs Delgado was on the ground with Mr Garcia's jacket under her head.

Her eyes were open, but her face was white.

'Silvia, my dear, you're safe,' she said, and took Silvia's hand. 'I'm happy now, I'm very happy ...'

Silvia took her mother's medicines out of the bag and gave her some. Mrs Delgado smiled.

'Thank you, dear,' she said.

Silvia sat and watched her. Mrs Delgado shut her eyes and slept.

5.1 Were you right?

Look again at the pictures in Chapter 6 and tick (✓) the right answer.

1 (page 24) What is the woman saying to Silvia?

   a 'Don't worry, you'll find her.'

   b 'I'll help you. We'll find her.'

2 (page 25) What is the angry man saying about Marco?

   a 'He helped a lot of people.'

   b 'He was only worried about his car.'

3 (page 26) What is Silvia thinking?

   a 'I'll easily find Mother here.'

   b 'I'll never find Mother here.'

4 (page 27) What is Mrs Delgado saying?

   a 'I'm happy now.'

   b 'I'm feeling very ill.'

5.2 What more did you learn?

Tick (✓) the right picture.

1 Which is a ruin?

2 Who pulls Marco from the rubble?

3 Who does Silvia love?

.3 Language in use

Look at the sentence in the box. Then finish the sentences from the story, below.

> Silvia **took** her mother's medicines out of the bag and **gave** her some.

1 She usually ....*caught*.......... (catch) a bus.

2 They all .... (have) the same idea.

3 I .... (come) back into town.

4 Behind them, more buildings .... (fall).

5 Other people .... (stand) and .... (talk).

6 She .... (can not) see very well in the thick smoke.

7 She .... (begin) to walk up and down the park.

8 Then suddenly, she .... (hear) her name.

9 Her eyes .... (be) open, but her face .... (be) white.

10 Mrs Delgado .... (shut) her eyes and .... (sleep).

.4 What happens next?

Look at the four pictures in Chapter 7. Then make these words into sentences about them.

1 ruins / There / at / are / work / in / the / of / a / building / men

....

2 her / Gabriel / shoes / finds / in / Silvia's / one / of / flat

....

3 but / There / is / some / no / milk / water / there / is

....

4 boy / talks / Gabriel / little / unhappy / an / to

....

Thieves

*It was his red rose. It was there, in the same place, by the
front door. A rose from another world, another life.*

It was early in the morning when
Gabriel arrived at the Delgados'
flat. His arm hurt badly, and he was
terribly thirsty.

The street was quieter now. Most
people were out in the country, or in
the parks outside the town. But there
were four or five men at work in the
ruins of the building next door. They
pulled the rubble away.

Gabriel watched them for a
minute. Suddenly, they stopped
working and listened.

'I can hear something!' one man
said. 'Here! I think it's a child. Quick! Come and help!'

Gabriel went to them.

'I can help,' he said.

One of them looked up and smiled at him.

'Don't be stupid,' he said. 'You've got to have two hands for this job.
Go and sit down.'

Slowly, Gabriel went up the stairs to the Delgados' flat. The building
was dangerous, but he didn't think about that. He could hear the cries of
the child. He felt terrible. Then he felt something on the floor under his
foot. He looked down. It was his red rose. It was there, in the same place,
by the front door. A rose from another world, another life.

The door of the flat was open. Gabriel called, 'Mrs Delgado! Silvia!
Are you there?'

There was no answer, but suddenly, two men ran out of the sitting-room. The first man went down the stairs before Gabriel could stop him. Then the other man ran past. Gabriel put out his foot and the man fell over it. A box fell to the ground. The man didn't stop. He jumped up and ran away.

Gabriel opened the box. There was jewellery inside it.

'Mrs. Delgado's jewellery!' he thought. 'So the **thieves** are busy now!'

He took the jewellery box into the flat. He looked round. The pictures were on the walls. Silvia's camera was on the table.

'Good,' he thought. 'The thieves didn't have much time. They only took the jewellery, and I've got it now.'

Then, near one of the armchairs, he saw Silvia's dirty evening shoes. He thought for a minute. For the first time for hours, he smiled.

'She wore those shoes last night,' he thought. 'So she came back here after the earthquake. She isn't dead! She came home, and took her mother to a safe place. Oh Silvia, Silvia, you're all right!'

thief /θiːf/ (n) *Thieves* take things from other people, but don't ask for them.

Gabriel forgot his broken arm, and the cut on his head. He was suddenly happy.

'I'll look for them,' he thought. 'They're out in the country. I know they are. I'll find them. I'll ...' He stopped. 'That's stupid,' he thought. 'I'll never find them. And I can't leave. There'll be other thieves later. I'll stay here and look after the flat.'

He went into the kitchen. There was no water, of course, but there was some milk.

Gabriel had a long, long drink and then felt better. His head and his arm hurt, but his legs felt stronger. And now he could think.

'It's not safe inside,' he thought. 'I'll stay in the street. Perhaps I can help the other men, and watch the building too.'

He went out of the flat and shut the door behind him.

◆

That day and the next day, Gabriel worked with the other men. He couldn't move the rubble, or pull people out of the ruins. But he could do other jobs.

The workers had to have food and drink. Gabriel found water and carried it to them. Then he looked for food. There was a shop at the end of the street. The windows and doors were broken. There was nobody there.

'The manager's dead,' a man told him.

Gabriel climbed through the broken door into the shop. He took some food and carried it back to the workers. The child from the ruins of the next building was safe now. She was in a car, on her way to hospital. But the workers didn't stop working. Other people were under the rubble. Gabriel could hear their screams.

He saw a small boy in the street, two or three years old. The child cried for his mother.

'She's at the hospital,' one of the workers said. 'We pulled her out. We didn't know about the child.'

Gabriel sat down next to the little boy and talked to him. He gave him some food and a drink of water. Slowly, the child stopped crying. Gabriel played with him for hours. Then his father came and took him away.

On the morning of the third day, firemen arrived.

For the first time, Gabriel stopped working. He couldn't do anything now. He sat down in front of the Delgados' door and fell asleep.

6.1 Were you right?

Look back at Activity 5.4. Then look at this picture and answer the questions.

a What did Gabriel do before this?

....

....

b What is he going to do next?

....

....

6.2 What more did you learn?

Finish the sentences. Write one word.

1 Gabriel can't help the other men because he has a .... arm.

2 It is dangerous, but he goes up the stairs to Mrs Delgado's ....

3 By the front door he finds his red ....

4 Two men run out with Mrs Delgado's ....

5 The second man falls over Gabriel's ....

6 Gabriel smiles when he sees Silvia's ....

7 Gabriel can't pull people out of the ...., but he can help the workers.

8 He can hear the .... of the people under the rubble.

9 He .... with a little boy for hours.

10 When the firemen arrive, Gabriel falls ....

.3 Language in use

Read the sentences in the box. Then finish the sentences with *stopped* or *started* and an *-ing* form.

> The workers didn't **stop working**.
>
> The child **stopped crying**.

1 Gabriel's arm hurt, but he .... (walk).

2 He .... (walk) when he saw the workers.

3 The men .... (work) when they heard a child's cries.

4 Then they .... (look) for the child.

5 Gabriel .... (worry) about Silvia when he saw her shoes.

6 He .... (help) the workers.

7 The boy .... (cry) when Gabriel gave him food and drink.

8 Gabriel .... (talk) to the boy when his father arrived.

.4 What happens next?

Read the name of Chapter 8 and the sentences below it in *italics*. Then look at the pictures. What are these people going to do next? What do you think? Make notes.

....
....
....
....
....

Home

There was a man asleep in front of her door. He looked thin and ill.
His face and clothes were dirty. And his arm ... his head ...

On the third day after the earthquake, good news came to Liberty Park. Mr Garcia had a radio in his car.

'Silvia, come and listen!' he called to her.

'There will not be another earthquake,' the newsreader said. 'People can go back to their homes. Dangerous buildings have a white **cross** on the door. Do not go inside those buildings. Other buildings are safe. I will say that again ...'

Mr Garcia and Silvia listened again. Then Mr Garcia turned the radio off.

cross /krɒs/ (n) X is a *cross*.

'Do you think it's really safe?' Silvia asked. 'Do you think we can go home?'

Mr Garcia shook his head.

'I don't know,' he said. 'But I know one thing. Your mother can't stay here. We'll take her home to her bed. You can look after her there.'

Everywhere in Liberty Park people asked questions. Many people were worried. Was the newsreader right? They were afraid of another earthquake. They wanted to stay in the country for another day or two. But other people wanted to go home. They started to move into the streets.

Silvia sat down next to her mother.

'We're going home, Mother,' she said.

Mr Garcia carried Mrs Delgado carefully to his car. She was as light as a child. Silvia opened the back door of the car, and Mr Garcia put Mrs Delgado inside.

The journey into town took a long time. There was rubble everywhere, and in some places there were trees across the road. Mr and Mrs Garcia sat in the front of the car and talked. They were worried about their flat, their friends and their neighbours. Silvia sat in the back with her mother and looked out of the window. But she didn't see the ruins, or the rubble, or the firemen. She didn't hear the Garcias.

'Will I see Gabriel again?' she thought.

The car turned into the Delgados' street and stopped outside their building.

'Look! Look! It isn't there!' said Mrs Garcia.

'What isn't there?' asked Silvia.

'The white cross! There's no white cross on our building. It's safe! We can go home!'

Mrs Garcia jumped out of the car and ran up the stairs to her flat. Mr Garcia smiled at Silvia.

'You go up first and open the door,' he said. 'My wife will come back in a minute. Then we'll carry your mother up the stairs.'

Silvia went into the building and up the stairs. Then she stopped.

There was a man asleep in front of her door. He looked thin and ill. His face and clothes were dirty. And his arm ... his head ...

'Gabriel!' she said.

Gabriel woke up and jumped to his feet. He didn't see Silvia in the dark. He only saw another thief!

'You can't come in here,' he said. 'This is the Delgados' home. No thieves here ...'

'Gabriel,' said Silvia again.

Gabriel stopped talking. His head was hot. His legs felt weak. He didn't want to fall now. Not now.

'Is it you?' he said. 'Is it really you?'

He had something in his hand. Silvia couldn't see it very well. Then she understood. It was a dirty, dead, red rose. She took it out of his hand.

'Thank you, Gabriel,' she said. 'It's beautiful.'

1 It is two days after Silvia and her mother arrive home. Gabriel is feeling better. Work with another student and have this conversation.

Student A | You are Silvia. You love Gabriel. Tell him why. You also understand more about Marco now. Tell Gabriel about him. Tell him your hopes for the future. Ask him about his plans.

Student B | You are Gabriel. Tell Silvia about the thieves in her mother's flat, the red rose and the dirty evening shoes. Ask her questions about Marco. Ask her about the future.

2 Discuss the pictures. What do you think really happens to Gabriel, Silvia and Marco after the story ends? Why? Think of another possible picture.

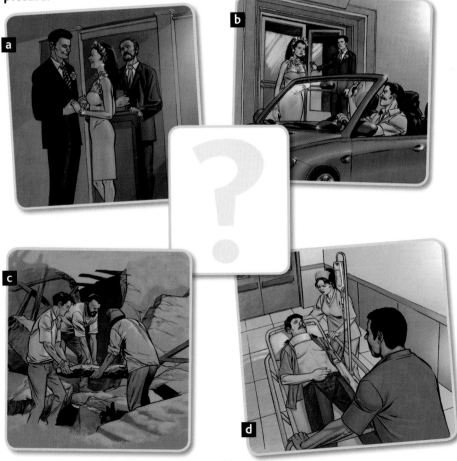

Write a letter from Silvia to Marco.

- Tell him how you feel about him now and why.
- Tell him about your plans with or without Gabriel.
- Tell him that you do or don't want to see him again.

Dear Marco,

Silvia

1 **Discuss earthquakes. How do they change people's lives? Make notes.**

Notes

2 **Where do earthquakes often happen? Look at these maps and write the names of the countries.**

1

3

2

....

3 **Read about this terrible earthquake and discuss this question. Why did it kill many, many people?**

Early on the morning of 26 December, 2004, an earthquake began under the sea, 160 kilometres from Sumatra, Indonesia. It was very strong and it happened suddenly. Nobody knew about it before it happened. The sea floor moved and pushed the water up 30 metres. This wall of water moved east and west, and in the next seven hours it arrived at the beaches of many Asian and African countries. It killed more than 225,000 people. More than 5,000,000 people lost their homes and had no clean water. People think that about one third of the dead were children.

4　Work with three or four other students. When people have news about an earthquake early, they can make plans. What can they do? Ask people, or look on the Internet. Then make notes.

Get ready before an EARTHQUAKE happens!

a) Put these in a box:
....
....
....

Think!
b) Where is the safest place inside your house?
....

c) Where is the safest place outside?
....

d) Which places, inside and outside, are dangerous?
....

Do you live near the sea?
After an earthquake at sea:
e) what will you feel under your feet?
....

f) what will you listen to?
....

g) what will you hear at sea?
....

h) what will you see, out at sea?
....

i) where will you go?
....
....

5 Some countries often have small earthquakes. But people in these places never know when there will be a big earthquake. Your town is in one of these places. Is it also near the sea? What can people do when they move into your town? What can they do when the ground starts shaking?

Write a page, with pictures, for your town's newspaper. But don't make people very unhappy about their move to the town!